Bird

by

Auriel Wyndham Livezey

Illustrated by

Bill Kuhre

MOUNTAINTOP
PUBLISHING

Cover and Illustrations: Bill Kuhre
Design and Layout: A.W.L.

Mountaintop Publishing
P.O. Box 15316
Long Beach, California 90815

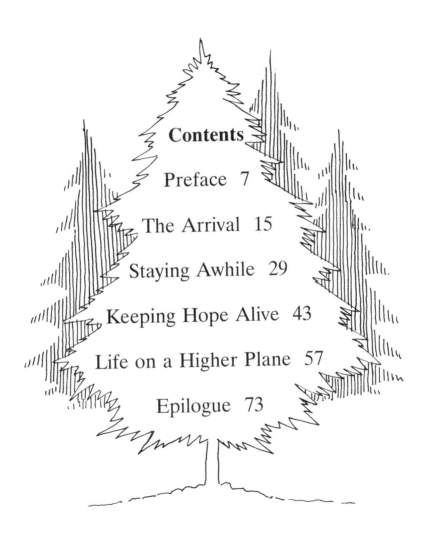

Contents

This book is dedicated
to all those who would
like to fly a little
higher.

Preface

It's difficult to say when the story of Bird actually began. It's almost as though he had been waiting backstage for his cue to walk out and play his part. But prior to this, before the couple in this story had moved up to the mountain and to the stage on which Bird would emerge, they had scenery in front of them that looked like a backdrop in a huge theatre. They lived in a house overlooking Pauma Valley, which rose up into Palomar Mountain.

The view was grand and expansive but, as they often remarked to each other, it almost seemed unreal. What was most real and tangible to them were life's most precious lessons, — the spiritual lessons they were learning. For instance, they were becoming more aware of what was influencing them. Were they being adversely affected by their own human desires and biases, by other people's opinions, or by world thinking in general? Or were they being motivated consistently by unselfishness and goodness? These were the kinds of questions the couple would deal with as they sat on the deck of the house overlooking the valley.

Now and then the couple would have unexpected company in the form of a coyote strolling through their property or a road runner zooming across the deck. And, of course, there were the many rabbits playing leapfrog over each other, their whiskers quivering with delight.

The couple lived rather simply, knowing how difficult it would be for anyone to grow spiritually, and gain true peace and happiness, while engrossed in the acquisition and care of material possessions. They enjoyed simplifying life, even if it was just replacing some ground cover, that the rabbits loved to eat bare, with gravel and stepping stones, which the rabbits then used as their main thoroughfare. This ensured peaceful coexistence for all concerned.

Preface

The opportunity to simplify even further came when the couple received a strong intuitive nudge to move up to the top of Palomar Mountain. In order to do this they sold the home with the view, including anything that wouldn't fit into their new home, — a little house nestled among tall trees.

However, the more basic lifestyle of the mountain involved a good amount of work, for they sawed their own wood for heat and baked their own bread. But doing without television during this period gave them ample time for quiet, unprogrammed contemplation. They saw more clearly how laws of goodness, God's laws, apply impartially to everyone, and in every human situation.

So they agreed together that mountaintop living is definitely a state of thought, not a geographical location, and that elevating lessons can be learned anywhere and at any time. An actual mountain just happened to be the right place for this couple at that time in their lives;

Preface

and they were so ready to learn that they even referred to their little mountain home as their classroom. It was into this classroom that a very different kind of example was introduced. The couple didn't realize it at the time, but they were on the brink of a new adventure and a brand-new lesson.

Bird

CHAPTER ONE

The Arrival

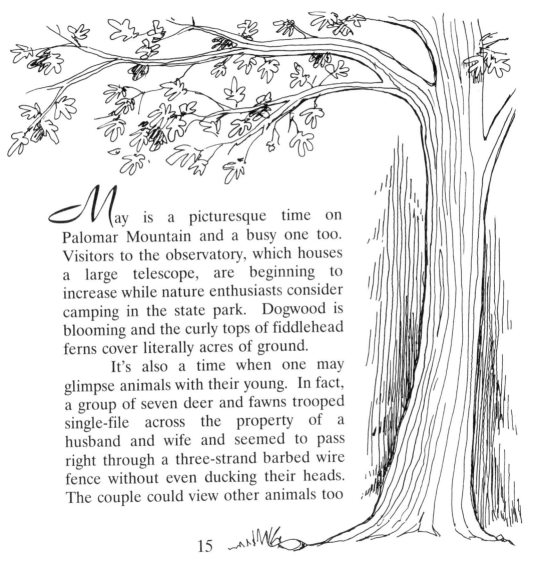

$\mathcal{M}$ay is a picturesque time on Palomar Mountain and a busy one too. Visitors to the observatory, which houses a large telescope, are beginning to increase while nature enthusiasts consider camping in the state park. Dogwood is blooming and the curly tops of fiddlehead ferns cover literally acres of ground.

It's also a time when one may glimpse animals with their young. In fact, a group of seven deer and fawns trooped single-file across the property of a husband and wife and seemed to pass right through a three-strand barbed wire fence without even ducking their heads. The couple could view other animals too

The Arrival

from time to time, for instance a bobcat, "Bob" for short, and a skunk, "S.K." The deer would bolt if spoken to, but Bob and S.K. would usually pause and listen for a few moments before ambling off.

The property itself was on top of the mountain near a state park and was comprised of ten acres of majestic oaks, pines and cedars; and right in the middle, looking like something out of a fairy tale, stood a very small house. It was three stories high and the stone bedroom on the first floor could have easily belonged to those cartoon characters, the Flintstones. One could go outside through the bedroom door and up stone steps to the front door and living room-kitchen level, or one could go up through a trapdoor in the bedroom and arrive right in the small kitchen. The third story was a cozy loft, and a massive stone chimney went from the first floor all the way up.

The Arrival

The couple enjoyed seeing the animals but never attempted to feed them, except with kind thoughts, so as not to deprive them of their independence. It was joy enough to see a doe with her fawn nibbling on acorns, while they watched quietly from the window.

However, of all the creatures on Palomar Mountain perhaps the most timid is the one the mountain is named for. According to a book of folk-lore "palomar" is an Indian word meaning "dove-cote." Now, these doves or Palomar pigeons are lovely large blue-gray birds, with a white band around their necks and a darker one across their beautiful fanlike tails, earning them the name of band-tailed pigeons. They would stay at a very safe distance from people, but now and then the husband and wife could see them drinking from the bird bath, some forty feet from the house. But viewing these

19

beautiful birds was only possible if the couple remained inside the house and stood very still at the window.

The previous owners of the property had been ships' captains and there was quite a collection covering a good portion of the acreage — things ranging from old cars to antique buggies to ship's paraphernalia. But now the land was totally cleared and the couple were just putting some finishing touches on a tool shed they had built.

Suddenly the wife noticed a little ball of fluff walking towards her, actually waddling like a duck would be more accurate. It was some kind of baby bird and was evidently all alone for there were no other birds around and no sign of a nest that they could see.

So they took it into the house and tried to feed it breadcrumbs moistened in water, but it seemed too young to be fed

The Arrival

like that and spat most of it out. This concerned the couple and so they prayed for the bird. But after two days when it was hardly retaining any food at all, they felt it should be returned to its natural environment. Hopefully, its parents would find it and care for it. This was not at all an easy decision for them to make, knowing what it was like out in the forest and the kinds of animals that were there.

So that afternoon, a Sunday, the husband took the little ball of fluff, walked quite a distance from the house over rough terrain, past tall trees and into a clearing filled with springtime grasses and weeds and left the little bird there.

The night seemed very long indeed and the couple didn't sleep too well at all. However, every time they thought of the little bird out there in the forest, they would pray and know that all of God's creatures were safe with Him.

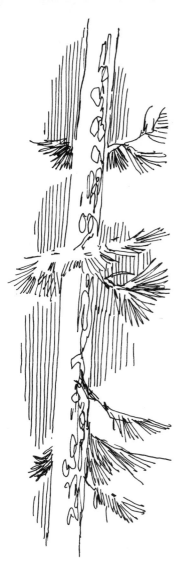

The Arrival

Well, morning finally came and the husband and wife were getting ready to go to their office in the city below. They were near the window in the living room on the second floor and were just about to walk out the door when they happened to glance down and see something on the concrete pad below. It was a little ball of fluff, standing there in front of their bedroom door as though it were waiting for them.

CHAPTER TWO

Staying Awhile

$\mathcal{Y}$es, the little bird was back, evidently to stay, at least for the present. To avoid becoming too personally involved with it, the couple decided not to give it a person or pet name but to simply call it "Bird."

After about a day or two Bird's eating habits improved tremendously and he was able to gobble down the wet breadcrumbs they offered him. And he sometimes moved his head in a strange forward motion, which was not totally unfamiliar. Then it dawned on them, and the mystery was solved. Bird was a band-tailed Palomar pigeon!

Staying Awhile

During the daytime Bird would stay in the house in his own little box, sometimes furnished with breadcrumbs in an eggcup, but usually his meals were taken at family times, three times a day, from a saucer on the kitchen counter. The husband and wife would take turns breaking a small piece off an English muffin, Bird's favorite bread, and putting it onto his saucer containing water.

His nighttime residence was in a small office about fifty feet from the house. This was formerly a woodshed which had suffered some damage from a falling limb of a tree, but had been completely restored utilizing rough wood planks for paneling and antique windows found on the property. With some country wallpaper and curtains it was now a presentable office. Bird's box was covered, except for a few inches, with a towel every night and when the couple

30

would arrive in the morning to see him, he would yawn and stretch, sometimes putting his foot through his wing. If a bird could smile and act happy to see someone, Bird certainly did that.

Although he was developing and his feathers were coming in on his wings and tail, he was nowhere near ready to fly. The couple still prayed for Bird and though they knew the best solution was always to trust God, they couldn't help feeling a good answer would be for his parents to find Bird and care for him. Then he could not only copy their eating and flying habits, but he could also learn to take precautions for his safety, things he would need to know in order to be out on his own in the forest one day.

The wife even took him out to a small rock a few times to try to teach him to fly, but he just hopped around instead, inspecting bugs and anything else that

33

looked interesting.

However, one day when in his box near the living room window, he became very excited, jumping up and down and flapping his wings. He had good reason to act that way for there on the electric wire in front of the house were two large beautiful band-tailed pigeons. It appeared as though the couple's prayers had been answered.

The wife took Bird outside, down the stone steps to the first landing and put him on the ground. Then she went back inside. All during this time the adult birds, usually so timid and skittish, never moved though they were quite close to the house. They just stared at Bird and Bird stared back.

The couple, hardly daring to breathe, watched from the window wondering what would happen next and how these birds could possibly take this

large baby bird with them. They certainly seemed to be the parents, or at the very least a good stand-in for them.

A few minutes passed in what you could only call a silent communication among the three. Then to the couple's amazement Bird suddenly turned around, walked back to the first step of the house and attempted to climb it. It was much too high for him, but he tried valiantly to hop up while the adult birds looked on most attentively. Feeling somewhat disappointed, the wife went out and put the little fellow back in his box, but at the same time she and her husband couldn't help but marvel at what had happened. It was just as though Bird had been told that he had to stay, that this was still his home for awhile.

So, again, Bird was back!

The adult birds were to put in a couple more appearances along the way.

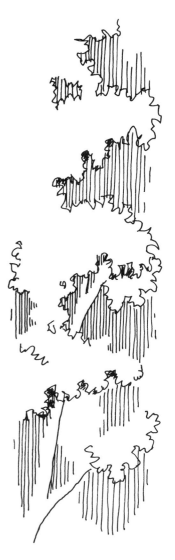

Staying Awhile

The next time they came was when Bird was just beginning to fly a little, almost as though they were there at his training session. And there were times when Bird would flap his wings in excitement and they were nowhere in sight. The couple had the feeling, however, that they were never too far away, even though unseen.

CHAPTER THREE

Keeping Hope Alive

$\mathcal{L}$ ife with Bird was most interesting, but the normal routine wasn't interrupted, and the couple went on with their work as usual. Things were progressing nicely but some really big challenges lay ahead.

The first one came about when Bird was on one of his training missions on the lower level by the bedroom. There was a wide path that went across that area, bounded on one side by wild lilac bushes and on the other by a little rock garden. Bird was practicing take-offs, short flying hops and rather ungainly belly-type landings.

43

Keeping Hope Alive

The man and his wife had watched for awhile from the living room window above and laughed at the performance, but then became engrossed in talking with each other. When next the wife glanced out she was shocked to see a large cat dragging Bird along the ground. As she rapped on the window and called out to it to stop, the husband raced out the door and down the steps. He returned with a very bedraggled looking bird.

It was not a good picture. Some of Bird's tail feathers were gone and his right wing hung limply at a strange angle. It appeared to be broken. However, all through this experience Bird remained peaceful, and it was evident that his feathers had only been ruffled on the outside. He held his head high and looked as expectant as ever.

It seemed as though the couple had more praying to do for Bird, and perhaps

even more for themselves not to be angry at the cat. It was obviously one of the wild cats on the mountain, that is, domestic cats that have left their homes and run loose looking for food.

The more the husband and wife were able to trust God and understand His loving care for all, the better Bird did until finally he seemed to be just about his old self again. The wing was healed and all he had to show for that whole episode were the missing feathers. However, he was almost back where he had started regarding his flying ability, but he patiently set about his flight training once again.

It was getting close to two months since Bird had first appeared on the scene, and he was now a handsome looking creature and quite grown up. His flying was improving too.

But one day when Bird was sitting on a rock outside, having flown his usual

three or four feet, a hawk suddenly appeared out of nowhere and swooping into the clearing, with his sharp talons and large body, flew directly into Bird, knocking him to the ground.

At that moment the husband just happened to look out the window and see what was going on. He called to his wife and this time he banged on the window to frighten the hawk who was now circling. The noise must have confused the hawk because, as he came in for the second time and latched onto Bird, he immediately dropped him. By the time the wife got there a small huddled mass lay on the ground.

It would do no good to describe the state the bird was in; it's just best to say it was pitiful. For two days he was unable to eat a thing and he was still bleeding somewhat. The couple kept on lifting their thinking above the sad scene

and tried very hard not to be impressed with it. Then they felt intuitively that Bird wanted to be outside. So the wife took him out and set him under a bush. She read a hymn to him five times, after which he just got up and limped slowly away from her through the underbrush.

It was a little difficult for the couple to still feel good about Bird as things certainly looked bleak. But again, for the next few days they went on with their work and listened even more diligently for good and uplifting thoughts from God.

It was now about three days since Bird had left and about five days since his last meal with them. The morning was beautiful and sunny, and the husband was busy talking on the telephone when the wife came in from the kitchen just in time to see a flurry of feathers alight on the railing of the deck behind her husband.

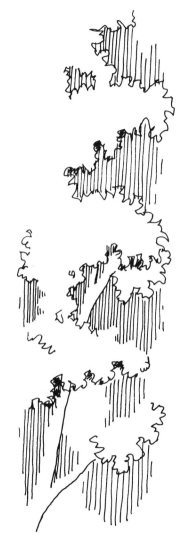

51

Keeping Hope Alive

Seeing the look on her face he turned around, and they both stared out the window at the beautiful big band-tailed pigeon that had flown in and was sitting on the rail about twelve feet above the ground.

Could it be. . . ?

CHAPTER FOUR

Life On A Higher Plane

*C*ould it really be Bird? The couple didn't move for a moment. Then they obviously came to a silent agreement. The husband was still on the telephone, and as he slightly nodded his head the wife smiled and opening the door she slowly approached the lovely band-tailed pigeon sitting on the railing of the narrow little deck. The bird remained still. When close enough she stretched out her hand to it, because this was how the couple had often carried Bird from place to place. This regal-looking creature stepped confidently from the railing onto her hand.

57

Life on a Higher Plane

Yes, it was Bird. He was back again! How the couple rejoiced as she brought him into the house. He was not only able to fly and fly well, but he was completely healed. They immediately fed him to show how happy they were to see him again, and they gently stroked his neck.

That night it was hard to know where Bird should be so they put him back in his box in the office, and Bird obediently went. But it was pretty obvious he was just humoring them for he was well able to be out on his own. So the next day they let him sit around outside and that night he flew off into the forest.

A day later while reading in the living room, they were startled by something that flew around the house three times so fast they couldn't see what it was till it landed. Well, it certainly couldn't be Superman. It wasn't a plane.

Life on a Higher Plane

No, it was Bird! He was no mean flyer, and his performance in circling the house reminded them of a little kid, who has mastered the art of bicycle riding, calling out, "Look, Ma, no hands!"

Now was this the end of the bird saga? Not quite yet, for Bird had something very interesting to share.

Bird would come back every morning and evening and take a little food on his saucer outside the house. He would sit between the couple as they took turns feeding him. However, he didn't eat very much at these times, most often just a few bites and off he would fly.

Well, one morning about seven o'clock, when the rays of the sun were just peeking over the tops of the tall trees and there was still a mountain chill in the air, the couple went out as usual with Bird's breakfast and sat down beside the rocks near the front door. Bird, who usually

waited on the rail or a nearby tree, immediately glided down. But he wouldn't touch the first piece of bread, instead he just sat there. Then he lifted his head and looked intently toward the sunrise. He was definitely in a listening mode, even cocking his head from side to side now and then.

The couple decided that they should listen too, which they did. So there they were, a man and a woman with a bird between them all sitting and listening and looking toward the sunrise. And though a cool breeze still stirred, there was hardly a movement among them. The couple heard wonderful ideas of good from God, and they felt sure that Bird was also hearing his own version of what that meant. He was helping them to listen better and see what feeding really means.

After about forty-five minutes, Bird

ended this lesson by eating two or three pieces of bread and then swiftly flying off straight as an arrow through the trees.

Bird's visits became more infrequent. Sometimes he only turned up for one meal a day, but even then it was mostly for listening. One time he appeared with a friend over the outdoor barbecue and watched the man as he cooked a meal. Another time when the couple were doing some work outside the office, they saw him on the roof. As they spoke to him and the wife held out her arm, he came down and alighted on it for a moment.

But one of the last sightings, and a truly memorable one, happened in August. This was during the period when the couple, feeling that it was now time to go, were making preparations to move from the mountain. They were grateful that Bird was off on his own and doing so well.

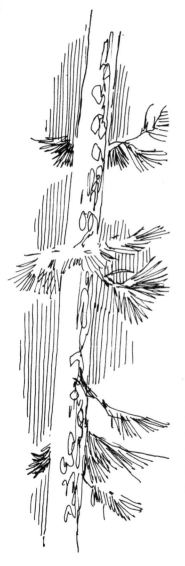

Life on a Higher Plane

It seemed that he had found his place in the forest. But there was more to it than that, as this incident showed.

This particular day the husband was walking down the driveway towards the outer fields and roadway. The wife, watching him from the window, became aware of movement in a tree above the driveway. On a branch sat Bird (she could tell by the missing tail feathers) and with him sat two beautiful big band-tailed pigeons, looking very like the ones who had visited him on previous occasions.

As the man passed beneath them, Bird sort of pointed toward him and all three birds turned their heads, following him as he walked along. They watched him intently until he rounded the bend and was out of sight. It was as if Bird were saying to them, "There he is, he's the one." The interest of the other two seemed almost like a bird "thank you."

Life on a Higher Plane

But perhaps it wasn't really that. Perhaps it was just their own peaceful, loving natures being seen together above the earth where they belonged.

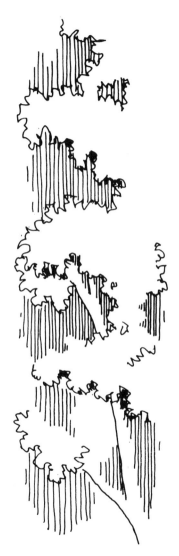

Epilogue

Soon after leaving the mountain, the couple took an apartment at the beach. They were grateful for all the wonderful things learned during their three years on the mountain, including the lessons Bird had taught them.

Bird appeared always to be connected to good, to God. He was always cared for and protected, even when he had his challenges. And he never reacted adversely to adverse conditions, but maintained his peace and his hopeful demeanor throughout. Nothing could really rob him of his pure intention to fly high. He had to fulfill his mission in life and he did.

It was during the stay at the beach that the couple noticed something that had never been apparent to them before, though obviously it was an occurrence that must have taken place in front of their very eyes dozens of times over.

Epilogue

The occurrence was simply this: The large flock of seagulls that inhabited that area all gathered together every morning on the beach, and in still silence they faced inland to view the rising sun. Then they would disperse for an active day of seeking out fish or pestering tourists for tidbits. Once more, in the evening, the flock would gather round and this time face the ocean, looking out toward the horizon and the setting sun. Again, the busy and rather raucous group would become quiet and respectful. Like Bird, they all appeared to be listening.

After a number of days of watching this, the couple decided to go down and join them. The gulls fluttered a little, moving nervously aside to accommodate their visitors. But after a moment all settled down in an agreeable fashion.

As the glow of the sun enveloped them all, the couple felt the joyful glow of understanding how some little creatures listen to goodness. They too enjoyed listening this way. It was one of the lessons Bird had taught them.